PHONICS

with
Daphne Dolphin

Stage 4

AGES 4-7

Contents

Join the letters to make the word.

Read the word. Hear the letter sounds.

s t o p

stop

Join the letters to make the words.

s t i ck   s t i ng   st a m p

_____   _____   _____

Label the pictures correctly.

_____   _____   _____

Join the letters to make the words and write them below. Draw a picture of the word.

_____   _____   _____

f a s t   n e s t   f i s t

2

PARENT'S TIPS

Help your child to build up each word. Which words begin with 'st'? Which words end with the same sound?

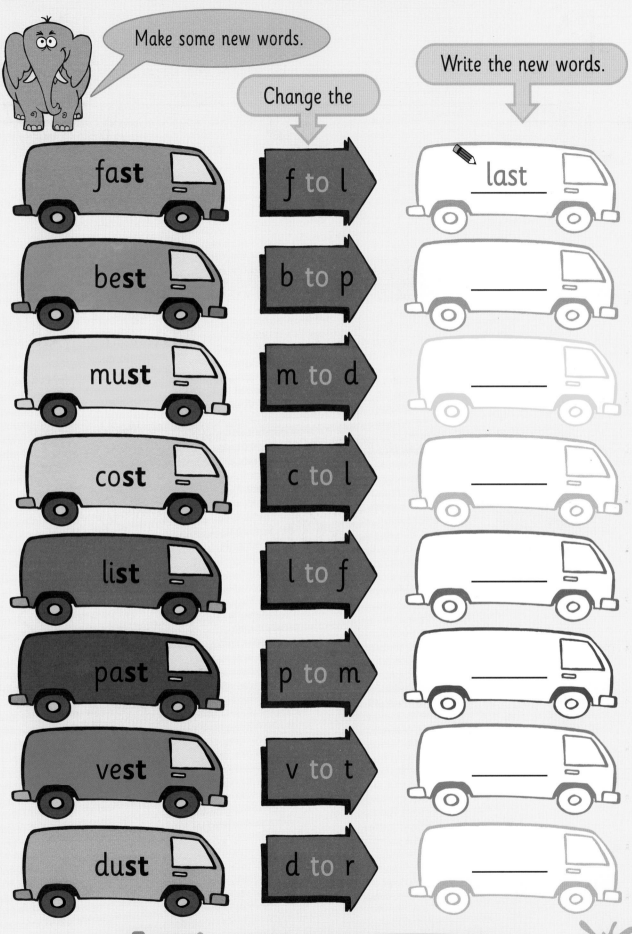

Make some new words.

Write the new words.

Change the

fast — f to l → last

best — b to p → _____

must — m to d → _____

cost — c to l → _____

list — l to f → _____

past — p to m → _____

vest — v to t → _____

dust — d to r → _____

PARENT'S TIPS Playing with words is an excellent way of helping your child experiment with sounds and learn how words are built up.

3

Join the letters to make the word.

Read the word. Hear the letter sounds.

sh **ee** p

sh**ee**p

Join the letters to make the words.

b **ee**

t r **ee**

th r **ee**

Label the pictures correctly.

Join the letters to make the words and write them below. Draw a picture of the word.

w **ee** p

s w **ee** p

s l **ee** p

PARENT'S TIPS

Explain that whenever the letters 'ee' come together in a word they make one sound.

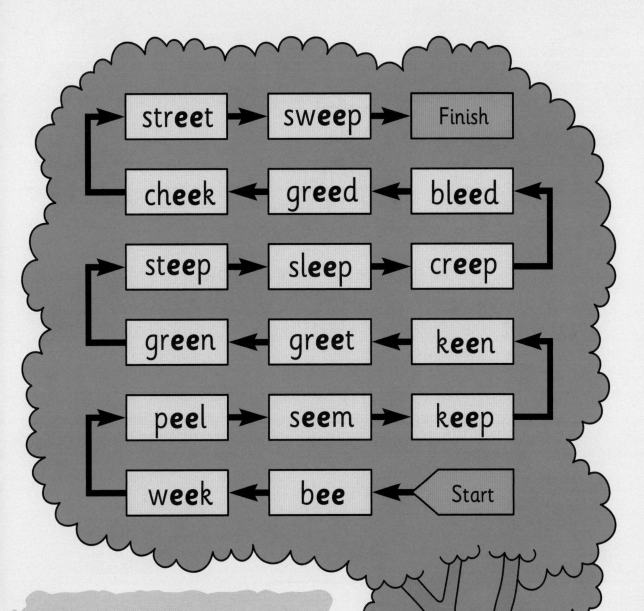

str**ee**t	→	sw**ee**p	→	Finish
ch**ee**k	←	gr**ee**d	←	bl**ee**d
st**ee**p	→	sl**ee**p	→	cr**ee**p
gr**ee**n	←	gr**ee**t	←	k**ee**n
p**ee**l	→	s**ee**m	→	k**ee**p
w**ee**k	←	b**ee**	←	Start

Climb the tr**ee**.
S**ee** who can get
to the top first!

- Play the game with a partner.
- You n**ee**d a counter each and a coin
- Take it in turns to spin the coin.
  Tails = move one space.
  Heads = move two spaces.
- If you can't read the word you land on, miss a turn.
- The first person to get to the top of the tr**ee** is the winner.

PARENT'S TIPS

Have a practice run first and help your child build and read each word before playing the actual game.

Join the letters to make the word.

Read the word. Hear the letter sounds.

s ea t

seat

Join the letters to make the words.

ea t   l **ea** p   s **ea** l

_____   _____   _____

Label the pictures correctly.

_____   _____   _____

Join the letters to make the words and write them below. Draw a picture of the word.

_____   _____   _____

r **ea** d   m **ea** l   b **ea** ch

6

PARENT'S TIPS

Explain that whenever the letters 'ea' come together in a word they make one sound. Look back at page 4 and ask your child what they notice about the 'ee' and 'ea' sounds. (They sound the same.)

How many **ea** words can you re**a**d?

Tick ✓ the words you can re**a**d.

No ch**ea**ting!

Super Re**a**der

e**a**t ☐	s**ea** ☐	b**ea**t ☐	n**ea**t ☐
h**ea**p ☐	l**ea**p ☐	b**ea**k ☐	sp**ea**k ☐
t**ea**m ☐	cr**ea**m ☐	m**ea**n ☐	cl**ea**n ☐
s**ea**l ☐	m**ea**l ☐	b**ea**st ☐	f**ea**st ☐
each ☐	t**ea**ch ☐	b**ea**ch ☐	**ea**sy ☐

20
19
18
17
16
15
14
13
12
11
10
9
8
7
6
5
4
3
2
1

Colour in your score.

Join the letters to make the word.

Read the word. Hear the letter sounds.

b r **ay**

br**ay**

Join the letters to make the words.

b **ay**   p **ay**   r **ay**

_____   _____   _____

Label the pictures correctly.

_____   _____   _____

Join the letters to make the words and write them below. Draw a picture of the word.

p l **ay**   t r **ay**   p r **ay**

8

PARENT'S TIPS

Notice that 'ay' makes one sound. Ask your child to trace the 'ay' in the air with their fingers, saying 'Hooray for ay' as they do so.

Use the words in the box below to answer the crossword.

ha**y**   **pay**   **s**a**y**   tr**ay**   spr**ay**
yesterd**ay**   cr**ay**on   Wednesd**ay**

across

5 the d**ay** before tod**ay**
6 something you use to colour in
7 to speak
8 to give money for something

down

1 what horses eat
2 the d**ay** after Tuesd**ay**
3 you carry things on this
4 water from a hose pipe

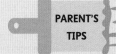 PARENT'S TIPS

Help your child to read all the 'ay' words in the box before attempting to do the crossword.

 9

Join the letters to make the word.

Read the word. Hear the letter sounds.

r | ai | n

r**ai**n

Join the letters to make the words.

t | r | **ai** | n   n | **ai** | l   **ai** | m

_____   _____   _____

Label the pictures correctly.

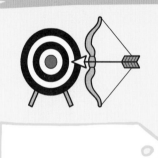

_____   _____   _____

Join the letters to make the words and write them below. Draw a picture of the word.

_____   _____   _____

s | n | **ai** | l   p | **ai** | n | t   ch | **ai** | n

10

PARENT'S
TIPS

Explain that whenever the letters 'ai' come together in a word they make one sound. Look back at page 8 and ask your child what they notice about the 'ay' and 'ai' sounds. (They sound the same – but the 'ay' always comes at the end of the word, whereas the 'ai' is always within each word.)

Write the correct sentence under each picture.

Here is a hammer with a **n**a**i**l.

Here is some water in a p**ai**l.

Here is a rat with a t**ai**l.

Here is a ship with a **s**a**i**l.

Here is some water in a pail.

PARENT'S TIPS

Talk about each picture with your child, before reading the captions and matching them with the corect pictures.

11

Join the letters to make the word.

Read the word. Hear the letter sounds.

c a k e

cake

Join the letters to make the words.

r a k e   l a k e   b a k e

_____ _____ _____

Label the pictures correctly.

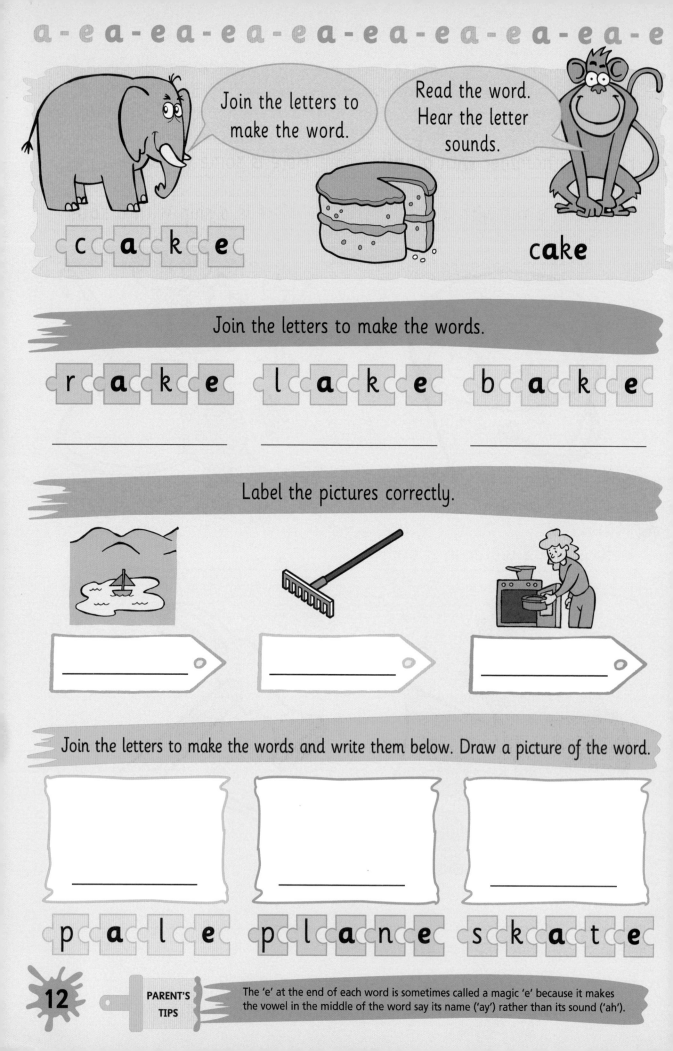

_____ _____ _____

Join the letters to make the words and write them below. Draw a picture of the word.

_____ _____ _____

p a l e   p l a n e   s k a t e

12

PARENT'S TIPS The 'e' at the end of each word is sometimes called a magic 'e' because it makes the vowel in the middle of the word say its name ('ay') rather than its sound ('ah').

Read the words.
Add **e** to each word.
Read the new words you m**ake**.

hat

rat

mat

 hate
_____

_____

_____

cap

tap

can

_____

_____

_____

Write the correct word under each picture.

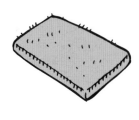

hat
_____

_____

_____

_____

_____

_____

Join the letters to make the word.

Read the word. Hear the letter sounds.

t r **y**

try

Join the letters to make the words.

c r **y**   d r **y**   f r **y**

_____   _____   _____

Label the pictures correctly.

_____   _____   _____

Join the letters to make the words and write them below. Draw a picture of the word.

f l **y**   s k **y**   sh **y**

PARENT'S TIPS

When 'y' comes at the end of some words it is sometimes pronounced like 'eye'.

Read the words and draw a picture.

a fly in the sky

my frying pan

someone crying

someone with an umbrella,
keeping dry

These pictures are by _____

PARENT'S TIPS
Begin by helping your child to read each picture caption. Don't forget to get your child to sign their masterpieces at the end!

15

Join the letters to make the word.

Read the word. Hear the letter sounds.

l | igh | t

light

Join the letters to make the words.

t | igh | t   r | igh | t   b | r | igh | t

_____   _____   _____

Label the pictures correctly.

[_____]   [_____]   [_____]

Join the letters to make the words and write them below. Draw a picture of the word.

[_____]   [_____]   [_____]

n | igh | t   f | igh | t   f | r | igh | t

PARENT'S TIPS
Explain that whenever the letters 'igh' come together in a word they make one sound. Look back at page 14 and ask your child what they notice about the 'y' and 'igh' sounds. (They sound the same.)

Find the ten **igh** words.

Write the words.

a	c	r	i	g	h	t	d	e	f

n	i	g	h	t	b	g	h	i	j

k	l	m	o	r	s	i	g	h	t

q	n	d	m	i	g	h	t	w	x

r	t	i	g	h	t	l	q	a	b

n	f	b	k	l	i	g	h	t	d

b	r	i	g	h	t	m	o	s	p

e	y	z	f	r	i	g	h	t	d

j	f	l	i	g	h	t	x	k	a

u	d	l	b	s	l	i	g	h	t

right

_____

_____

_____

_____

_____

_____

_____

_____

_____

PARENT'S TIPS   Ask your child to be a 'word detective' and look for the 'igh' words 'hiding' on the page. Developing a good eye for words is an important element of reading and spelling.

17

Join the letters to make the word.

Read the word. Hear the letter sounds.

h i v e

hive

Join the letters to make the words.

f i v e   d i v e   d r i v e

_____   _____   _____

Label the pictures correctly.

_____   _____   _____

Join the letters to make the words and write them below. Draw a picture of the word.

b i k e   n i n e   k i t e

18

PARENT'S TIPS

The 'e' at the end of each word is sometimes called a magic 'e' because it makes the vowel in the middle of the word say its name ('eye') rather than its sound ('ih').

Read the words.
Take the **e** off each word and
write the new word below.
Read the new words.

bite   **ripe**   **pine**   **wine**

✏️ bit
_____   _____   _____   _____

ride   **slide**   **spine**   **slime**

_____   _____   _____   _____

Write the correct word under each picture.

✏️ bite
_____

_____

_____

_____

_____

_____

PARENT'S TIPS Read the words at the top of the page with your child and then take off the magic 'e'. These words demonstrate clearly how the magic 'e' works.

19

Join the letters to make the word.

Read the word. Hear the letter sounds.

r oa d

roa d

Join the letters to make the words.

b oa t

c oa t

g oa t

_____

_____

_____

Label the pictures correctly.

_____

_____

_____

Join the letters to make the words and write them below. Draw a picture of the word.

_____

_____

_____

s oa p

l oa f

t oa d

PARENT'S TIPS

Explain that whenever the letters 'oa' come together in a word they make one sound. Help your child to work out and read the words on the page to demonstrate this.

oaoaoaoaoaoaoaoaoaoaoaoaoa

**Complete each word with oa.
Match the shapes.**

**Write the rhyming words
from the matching shapes.**

b__oa__t

g__l

cl__k

t__d

f__l

fl__t → boat   float

m__n

t__st

r__d

s__k

b__st

c__x

h__x

gr__n

PARENT'S TIPS After joining up the pairs of rhyming words, see how many others you can think of. Make up some rhymes with some of the words e.g. A boat can float.

21

Join the letters to make the word.

Read the word. Hear the letter sounds.

s n **ow**

sn**ow**

Join the letters to make the words.

r **ow**

_____

m **ow**

_____

sh **ow**

_____

Label the pictures correctly.

_____

_____

_____

Join the letters to make the words and write them below. Draw a picture of the word.

_____

_____

_____

b l **ow**

g r **ow**

s l **ow**

PARENT'S TIPS

Look back at page 20 and ask your child what they notice about the 'oa' and 'ow' sounds. (They sound the same – but 'oa' always comes within a word whereas 'ow' often comes at the end of a word.)

- Play the game with a partner.
- You need two counters and a coin.
- Take it in turns to spin the coin.
- Tails = move one space. Heads = move two spaces.
- If you can't read the word you land on, miss a turn.
- The first person to reach the finish is the winner.

Follow the arrows!

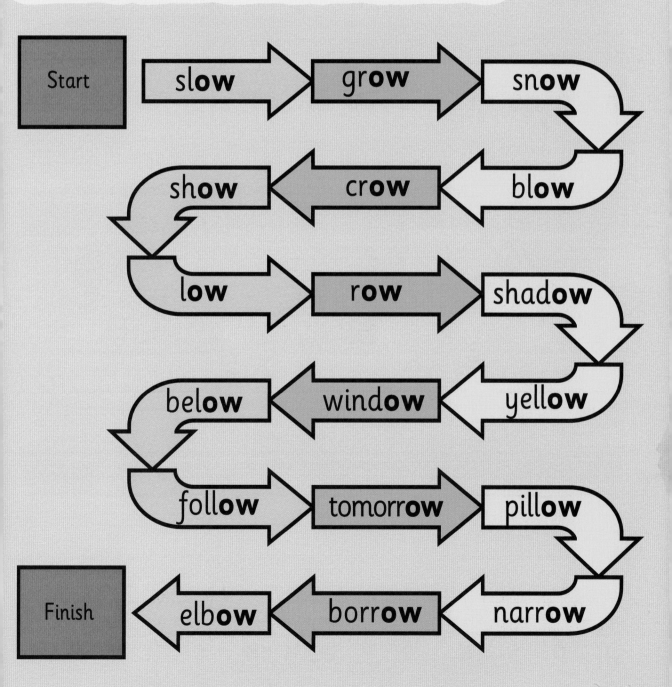

Start

slow → grow → snow

show ← crow ← blow

low → row → shadow

below ← window ← yellow

follow → tomorrow → pillow

Finish ← elbow ← borrow ← narrow

PARENT'S TIPS — Have a practice run first and help your child build and read each word before playing the actual game.

23

Join the letters to make the word.

Read the word. Hear the letter sounds.

h o s e

hose

Join the letters to make the words.

n o s e   b o n e   h o l e

_____   _____   _____

Label the pictures correctly.

_____   _____   _____

Join the letters to make the words and write them below. Draw a picture of the word.

_____   _____   _____

r o p e   s t o n e   s m o k e

24

PARENT'S TIPS

The 'e' at the end of each word is sometimes called a magic 'e' because it makes the vowel in the middle of the word say its name ('owe') rather than its sound ('oh').

Join the pairs of words.

hop	**c**o**de**
mop	**n**o**te**
cod	**h**o**pe**
rob	**sl**o**pe**
not	**m**o**pe**
slop	**r**o**de**
rod	**r**o**be**

Write the words.

hop   hope

_____

_____

_____

_____

_____

Use some of the words in these sentences.

1 I ____hope____ you are happy.

2 I wr**ote** a _____ .

3 You catch a fish with a _____ .

4 I _____ my bike yesterday.

5 A _____ is something you wear.

6 You wash the floor with a _____ .

PARENT'S TIPS The activity at the top of the page clearly demonstrates how the magic 'e' works and affects the sound of the vowel in the middle of the words.

25

Join the letters to make the word.

Read the word. Hear the letter sounds.

z **oo**

z**oo**

Join the letters to make the words.

p **oo** l   b **oo** t   r **oo** f

_____   _____   _____

Label the pictures correctly.

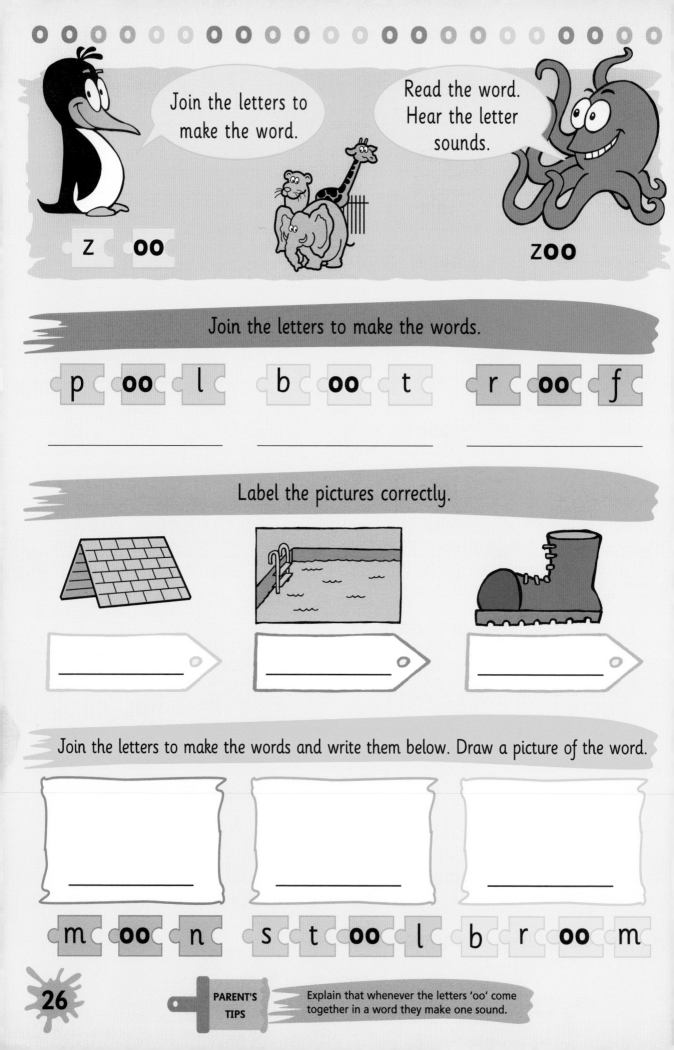

_____   _____   _____

Join the letters to make the words and write them below. Draw a picture of the word.

_____   _____   _____

m **oo** n   s t **oo** l   b r **oo** m

26

PARENT'S TIPS

Explain that whenever the letters 'oo' come together in a word they make one sound.

Use the words in the box below to answer the crossword.

z**oo**   b**oo**t   h**oo**f   p**oo**l
p**oo**r   br**oo**m   sp**oo**n   sch**oo**l

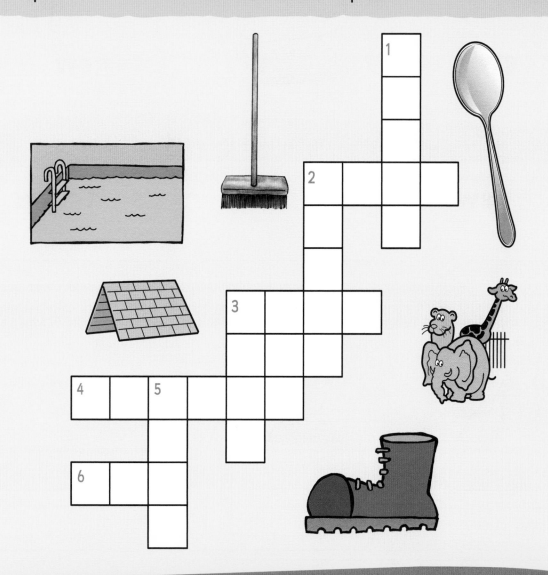

across

2 You wear it on your foot
3 You swim in it
4 A place where you learn
6 A place where you find lots of animals

down

1 you eat soup with it
2 you sweep with it
3 not rich
5 a horse's foot

PARENT'S TIPS   Help your child to read all the 'oo' words in the box before attempting to do the crossword.

27

Join the letters to make the word.

Read the word. Hear the letter sounds.

n **ew**

new

Join the letters to make the words.

ch **ew**   f **ew**   s t **ew**

_____   _____   _____

Label the pictures correctly.

[label]   [label]   [label]

Join the letters to make the words and write them below. Draw a picture of the word.

_____   _____   _____

d r **ew**   f l **ew**   s c r **ew**

PARENT'S TIPS

Look back at page 26 and ask your child what they notice about the 'oo' and 'ew' sounds. (They sound the same – but 'oo' always comes within a word whereas 'ew' often comes at the end of a word.)

- Play this game with a partner.
- You will need two counters and a coin.
- Take it in turns to spin the coin.
- Tails = move one space. Heads = move two spaces.
- If you can't read the word you land on, miss a turn.
- The first person to reach the end of the snake is the winner.

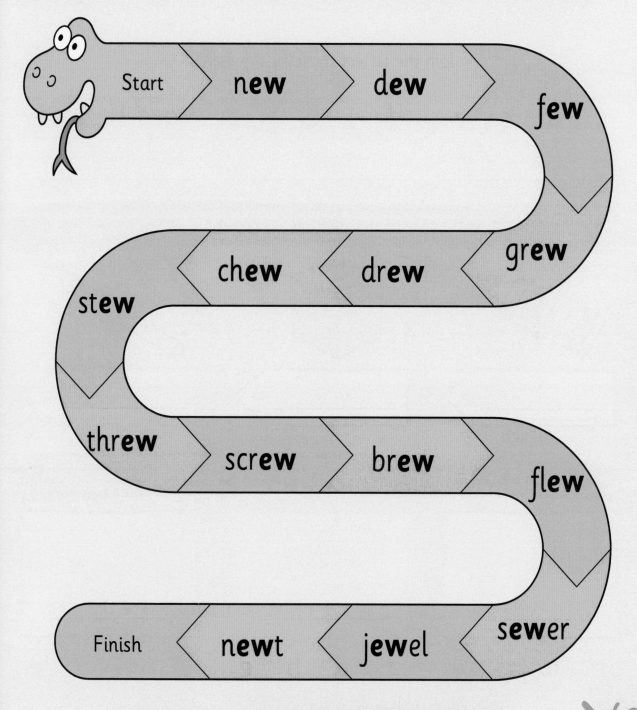

Start new dew few grew drew chew stew threw screw brew flew sewer jewel newt Finish

PARENT'S TIPS   Have a practice run first and help your child build and read each word before playing the actual game.

Join the letters to make the word.

Read the word. Hear the letter sounds.

m u l e

mule

Join the letters to make the words.

c u b e   f l u t e   g l u e

_____   _____   _____

Label the pictures correctly.

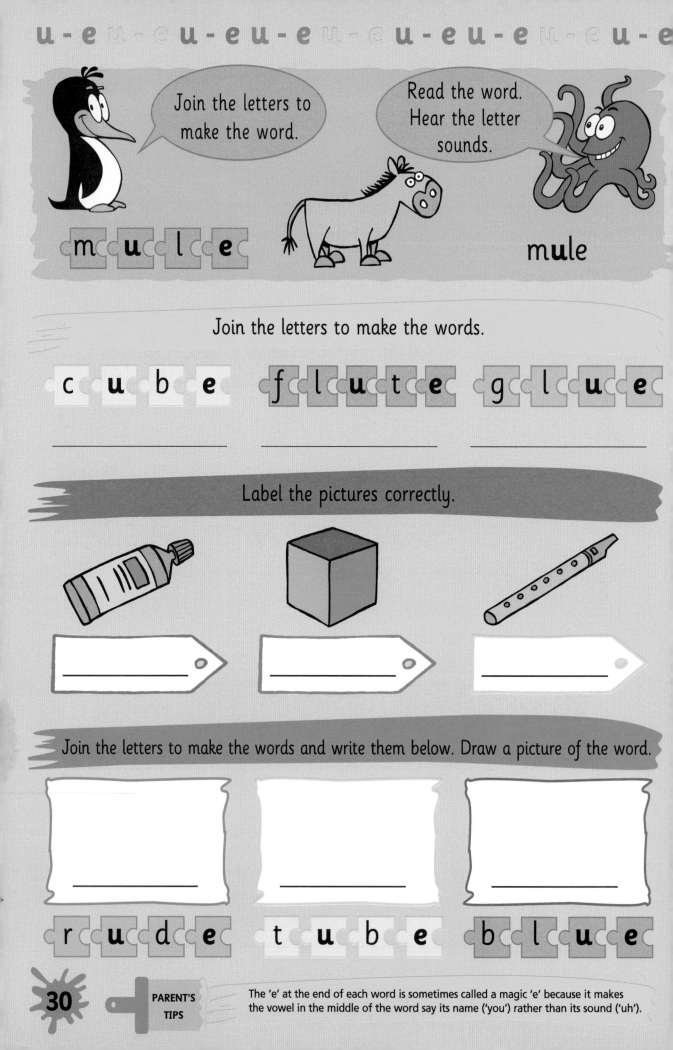

_____   _____   _____

Join the letters to make the words and write them below. Draw a picture of the word.

_____   _____   _____

r u d e   t u b e   b l u e

PARENT'S TIPS The 'e' at the end of each word is sometimes called a magic 'e' because it makes the vowel in the middle of the word say its name ('you') rather than its sound ('uh').

Read the words.
Add **e** to each word and write
the new word below.
Read the new words.

tub

cub

cut

tube

_____

_____

us

hug

plum

_____

_____

_____

Write the correct word under each picture.

use

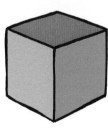
_____

_____

_____

_____

_____

PARENT'S
TIPS

Read the words at the top of the page with your child and then add the
magic 'e'. These words demonstrate clearly how the magic 'e' works.

31

Join the pairs of words.

Write the words.

cube — rule

tune   tube

mule   fluke

flute   June

duke   plume

fume   cute

cube   tube

PARENT'S TIPS

After joining up the pairs of rhyming words, see how many others you can think of. Make up some rhymes with some of the words e.g. Is it rude to run about nude?